:Spilling the Beans on...

Albert Einstein

and other clever clogs
(relatively speaking)

Christian
Smith

First published in 2000 by Miles Kelly Publishing,
Bardfield Centre, Great Bardfield, Essex CM7 4SL

Printed in Hong Kong

Copyright © Miles Kelly Publishing Ltd 2000
This edition printed in 2005 by Bardfield Press

ISBN 1-84236-482-0

2468109753

Cover design and illustration: Inc
Layout design: Mackerel
Art Direction: Clare Sleven

Spilling the Beans on...

Albert Einstein

and other clever clogs (relatively speaking)

by Fran Pickering

Illustrations   Mark Davis

About the Author

Fran Pickering is a full-time writer of non-fiction books, mainly for children and teenagers. Her most recent projects include an encyclopedia of animals, and a regular recipe column in the *Sunday Post*. She has worked as a nursery nurse, and writing for children after having her own family. She lives in the Lake District, and her interests include the unexplained and UFOs, science fiction and fantasy.

Contents

Chapter 1

A strange name – and a large brain!

First, some German!

The German word for 'one' is 'ein'.

The German word for 'stone' is 'stein'.

So if the great scientist Einstein had been born in England he would have been called Albert Onestone!

Funny name or not, we know that Albert was born with an exceptional brain. For instance when he died in 1955, aged 76, the pathologist, a Dr Thomas Harvey, took his brain out, photographed it and then pickled it like a large gherkin!

Well, it was preserved in formalin which, where brains are concerned, is the same process.

Not content with pickling, scientists then chopped his brain up into 240 cubes and numbered each one.

After that it sat in two jars in an office for 22 years, until scientists from McMaster University in California decided to study the bits and the photographs.

They found that part of Einstein's brain, the bit we use for mathematical reasoning, was wider than 70 other, non-genius, brains they also studied. It was also a different shape, not split by a groove that the rest of us have. This, they think, meant that more electrical circuits could be made, allowing Einstein to make better thought connections than the rest of us. So, for brains at least, 'groovy' is not so groovy!

In the case of young Albert Einstein, not so groovy was not so obviously bright either.

The young Albert

Albert Einstein was born in Ulm, Germany, in 1879 to a middle-class Jewish family. Hermann Einstein, Albert's father, owned a small shop that made electric machinery. He found it hard to sell the machines and so the family moved to Munich when Einstein was one year old.

No one would have known the young Albert Einstein was

a genius in the making; he did not talk until he was four years old and when he did speak his lips would move silently while he practised a whole sentence before he said it. He didn't read until he was nine and his parents were worried that they had a backward child.

Not talking much didn't mean he wasn't thinking. Albert was always a great thinker. Lonely and shy as a child he played by himself in the parks and woods and had lots of time to think about nature and the world around him. He wanted to know the how and why of things:

How do we see light from the stars? Why is every raindrop larger than four centimetres in diameter shaped like a parachute? In all fairness, the unusual shape of Einstein's brain may have been the reason he had trouble with words.

He once said that he always had such clear pictures of everything inside his head that he didn't need words in order to think.

When his sister Maria was born the two-year-old Albert was disappointed; he had been expecting a new toy. But they grew to be firm friends and throughout his life 'Maja' was the person he confided in the most. Someone who knew them when they were old, described how they would sit for hours, so alike with their heads of wild hair, talking and talking.

Even as a small boy Einstein was self-sufficient and thoughtful. His sister remembered the hours he would spend building up houses of cards into tall towers. He loved mechanical toys and really enjoyed jigsaw puzzles.

When he was four his dad gave him a magnet and, a year later, when Albert was ill in bed, a compass. Einstein liked to tell the story of the "wonder" of the compass. The fact that the needle would always swing to the north, guided by an invisible force, made a great impression on the small boy.

The compass convinced him that there had to be "something behind things, something deeply hidden." Experimenting with the magnet and the compass set Albert's imagination off on a track that took him, years later, to discoveries that changed the course of scientific knowledge.

For Albert Einstein, the road to the stars was paved with questions.

I HAVE NO SPECIAL GIFT. I AM JUST PASSIONATELY CURIOUS ABOUT EVERYTHING.

Schooldays

At age five Albert was sent to a local Catholic school. Although the family were Jewish, Albert's parents thought it more important to send him to a school that was near-by and where the fees were lower, than to find a Jewish school for him.

At age six the young Albert was given a violin. He took to it like a duck to water and for the rest of his life played both for pleasure and as a way to unwind from all that thinking! As an adult he was slightly arrogant about his musical talent and would stop playing if he thought people were not listening fully. Once, when asked if he counted the beat as he played, he replied, "Heavens, no. It's in my blood."

Einstein's uncle was an engineer who went on to study medicine. While he was a medical student, he was always on the look-out for a free meal, like all students the world over. He found one once a week at the Einstein home. He would talk for hours to the boy and it was he as much as anyone who fired Albert's imagination for the mysteries of the world we live in.

When Albert was 12 one of the school textbooks for that year was on Euclidean geometry. Euclid was a Greek mathematician who discovered relationships between straight lines and angles that teachers have made a beeline for ever since. All you'd hear from most kids when given such a book

Albert was a great thinker – but he felt his teachers were more interested in keeping pupil's quiet than teaching them much. Needless to say this got him into trouble. he hated the teachers – and they didn't like him much either.

So the headmaster made his decision. Albert was thrown out after only one term of the year.

Before we leave this tale of Albert's schooldays however, there is an interesting little fact.

During World War Two the school was bombed. After the war it was rebuilt. By now Albert was world-famous and yes, you've guessed right again. The new building was renamed – The Albert Einstein School!

To get back to 1895. When Albert got to Italy he loved it.

He said, "The people of northern Italy are the most civilized people I have ever met." He spent his spare time visiting art galleries and museums, going to concerts and lectures and reading book after book. That year in Italy gave him plenty of time to think.

At the end of the year Albert, now aged sixteen, sat an entrance exam for the Swiss Polytechnic in Zurich, the bustling capital city of the German-speaking part of Switzerland. He failed the arts section and was refused a place. But, even the worst scholars can make good in the end and Albert Einstein gave the world of science enough pushes in the back to get us where we are today. So, take heart – next time you get zilch out of ten for a maths test, just remind yourself you may yet be a genius in the making!

Someone suggested he try and get into a Swiss school in Aarau, a town about twenty miles west of Zurich. Most kids would not be queuing up to get back to school, but Albert was different and this school he loved. The teachers treated him well and his ideas were set free. His thoughts turned to the theory of electromagnetism formulated by James Clerk Maxwell. This was not taught much even in universities at the turn of the century, and the door to the universe opened even wider for Albert.

While at Aaru, Einstein stayed with Professor Winteler who ran the school. Professor Winteler was himself quite an unusual person and would often take the students for walks on in the mountains.

While at that school Einstein wrote an essay in French at the age of 16, explaining why he would like to study theoretical mathematics or physics:

"Above all it is my individual disposition for abstract and mathematical thought, my lack of imagination and practical talent. My inclinations have also led me to this resolve. That is quite natural; one always likes to do things for which one has talent. And then there is a certain independence in the scientific profession which greatly pleases me."

A. Einstein

Student Days

Aged 17, Albert left high school and this time managed to get into the Zurich Polytechnic. Albert spent most of his time at college in the laboratory skipping lectures. Luckily for him he made a good friend at the Polytechnic, Marcel Grossman. While Einstein worked in the library or the laboratory, Grossmann took excellent notes at the mathematics lectures, and gladly shared them with his friend before examinations.

Einstein later wrote,

I would rather not speculate on what would have become of me without these notes.

In 1900 Albert graduated as a secondary school teacher of maths and physics, but only just and probably to the surprise of the tutors who thought he was clever but cocky. One, Professor Pernet, said, "You have one fault – one can't tell you anything." At least Albert found out one thing though – that what he enjoyed doing most was studying physics. Only there could he "seek out the paths that lead to the depths."

Einstein wrote down his first thoughts on relativity at the Polytechnic. When he handed in his paper, it was returned because it was too short. He added one sentence, and it was then accepted.

When he was at Zurich Polytechnic, the handsome and witty Albert Einstein and Mileva Maric, a student from Serbia, fell in love. Mileva did Einstein's university homework and gave up her own career to help him. Letters they wrote to each other show that some of the ideas

Einstein developed were hers, but she let him have all the credit.

After leaving college in 1901 Albert found it very hard to get a good job, but even so, he had a busy year. First of all he became a Swiss citizen. Then he and Mileva went to Italy for a romantic holiday and Mileva became pregnant. She went back to her parents home in Hungary while Albert finally found a job in Scaffhausen, Switzerland, as a tutor. Later he moved to Bern.

Family life

In January 1902 Albert and Mileva's daughter, Lieseri was born. They decided to put her up for adoption and rumours went round that the child was ill and had died. Einstein was still wandering around from job to job and felt he was a burden on his family, who weren't very well off. Einstein's father died in this year and Albert, in despair, wondered if he had been mistaken in trying to become a physicist.

Finally he got a position at the Swiss Patent Office in Bern. It was "a kind of salvation," he said. The regular salary and the interesting work looking at the weird and wonderful gadgets people wanted to patent

cheered him up. He also now had spare time to do what he enjoyed most – think about the universe, and he began to publish scientific papers.

At the Patent Office Einstein made a new friend, Michele Besso. The two of them walked home together every day. Einstein thought him "the best sounding board in Europe" for scientific ideas. With other friends in Bern, Konrad Habricht, Maurice Solovine, Einstein and Besso met regularly to read and discuss books on science and philosophy. They called themselves the Olympia Academy, mocking the official science groups.

Chapter 3

"Change your clothes!"

"There's only one person he hasn't got time for – that's me!"
This is what Mileva Einstein said to a friend. What's more
she really meant it.

By now it was 1904. Albert and Mileva had married in
1903 and now, a year later, their first son, Hans Albert, was
born in Bern. Albert was so busy teaching and doing
research he hardly had any time for his wife.

So Mileva complained. She had good reason. Albert spent
so much time thinking that he would forget to eat – and

even worse – change his clothes!

Mileva would look at this wild-haired husband of hers, in his loose overshirt and baggy trousers tied with string, and she would get mad.

"I am starved of love", she used to say.

1905 was the big year for Albert. He was 26 years old and he published his Special Theory of Relativity – which was one in the eye for the school that threw him out. Maths teachers the world over learn that $e = mc^2$. It's something they never forget, and maths lessons have not been quite the same since.

Even after this Einstein was still thinking and questioning. He said: "I want to know how God created this world. I am not interested in this or that phenomenon, in the spectrum of this or that element. I want to know *His* thoughts; the rest are details." !!

A STORM BROKE LOOSE IN MY MIND!

So what was all the fuss about?

Some of the things that Einstein discovered about the Universe are now part of our basic knowledge, so it can be hard to understand all the amazement and "Wow! Blow my mind!" reactions from scientists at the time. But even Einstein said, "A storm broke loose in my mind," as he thought about these things.

1905

Einstein said that the pull of gravity and motion (movement) can change time and space. He did this in two separate brain buzzes: one in 1905, when he worked out the motion bit and in 1916 he had another brainstorm and added gravity to this theory. All of this chunk of information is known as the General Theory of Relativity but in 1905 he was only halfway there.

Einstein claimed that the four people who had impressed him the most and had the greatest effect on the way he thought were:

1916

Galileo

Galileo, the famous Italian astronomer who lived in the 16th and 17th centuries and was tortured for saying that the Earth moved round the Sun. Up until then the official view of the universe was that everything was fixed in place in layers. The Catholic Church had even had this written down

as one of the things they claimed to be true, but then along came this upstart with another version of reality. The Church couldn't afford to look wrong or foolish – they were afraid they might lose some of their power over people – so they tortured Galileo and made him say he was wrong. It turned out that he wasn't though!

James Maxwell

He was a British mathematician living in the 19th century, who worked out an explanation of electricity and magnetism.

Hendrik Lorentz

Hendrik Lorentz, a Dutch scientist (1853-1928) who tried to explain how electrons moved. He didn't get it right but his ideas gave Einstein a jumping-off point.

Isaac Newton

Isaac Newton lived in the 17th and 18th centuries. His claim to fame is that one day, while idling around under a tree, an apple fell and whacked him on the head. At this point most people would have seen stars, but Newton saw the light – and developed an interest in moving objects. He wrote down three of his main discoveries, which became known as Newton's Laws of Motion. They are the building blocks of ideas that Einstein stood on to reach the stars. They are:

1 **Inertia and Momentum** (movement): this means that objects at rest, stay at rest, unless something happens to make them move! I know, I know, this seems like discovering the obvious, but that's what a lot of this is about; finding ways to describe the obvious that will help us to move on and discover the not so obvious.

Try this experiment with someone.

- Put your hand on a flat surface, like a table top. Get a friend to balance a large, heavy book on your hand, with the end of the book resting on the table top.

- Now get your friend to whack as hard as they can with the flat of their hand on the book.

What happens?

If you do this right, nothing should happen! The book should stay in place and you won't feel anything in your hand. This is because the force that hit the book was not enough to make it move, or to travel through the book to your hand.

If you had balanced a grape on your hand, at the end of the experiment you'd have ended up with a stinging hand topped by a mushy mess!

So you see, whether a still object moves or not depends on the amount of force that hits it. Scientists would say that it is relative to the amount of force exerted on it. *(Remember this one!)*

The same rule applies to a moving object. If you are playing cricket or baseball and it is your turn to bat, the ball comes whizzing towards you in one direction and at one speed until you whack it and send it off in a different direction. *(Hopefully!)*

2 Acceleration: the next thing Newton took a look at was acceleration. Now to most of us, that means getting faster, but to scientists, who always like to be different, it means going faster *and* going slower! Going faster they call positive acceleration and going slower they call negative acceleration.

Newton discovered that whether something goes faster or slower depends on the amount of force exerted on it. *(Recognise this?)*

A force is basically a push or a pull

A push speeds things up – unless you are pushing against something moving fast towards you, in which case your push will slow the object down.

A pull will slow objects down – unless you are pulling something that is still and your pull starts it moving.

> **You'll soon discover that a lot of science is the trick of juggling two opposite things in your mind at the same time!**

Which brings us to Newton's Third Law:

3 **Action–Reaction:** imagine you are playing marbles. You roll your shooter at a stationary marble. Hitting the still marble slows yours down but your shooter makes the other marble start to roll. Scientists would say that your marble exerted a force on the marble at rest and caused it to accelerate. In other words, both marbles had exerted a force on each other and caused a reaction in each other. So you could say that:

FLICK

> **for every action there is an equal and opposite reaction. You could say it; scientists would say it!**

All these laws apply to things that go up and down
as well.

Try this: drop a ball.

When the ball is in your hand it is still;
its movement is zero. As soon as you let
go of it, it goes from zero movement to
some movement, so it accelerates.

The speed at which things fall is due to
the pull, or gravity, of the Earth as they
fall towards it.

Now try this: drop a flat sheet
of paper.

Does it fall as fast as the
ball?

Now do this: crumple the
paper into a ball and drop it.

Does it fall faster or slower
than the flat sheet?

It fell faster. Why? It must have
something to do with what it is falling
through – air.

The flat sheet of paper had a bigger
surface to be supported by air.

So – air and gravity are both forces and anything falling is
in a 'push me – pull you' situation, being pulled down by
gravity and pushed up by air at the same time.

So what has this got to do with Einstein? Lots, because Einstein looked at Newton's Laws and thought there ought to be one law that explained everything. Scientists call it the 'grand unified theory' and they are still searching for it today.

However, as he searched, Albert Einstein found many other bits of information to add on to Newton's list. One of the most important of these is his General Theory of Relativity. But more about that later!

If there's one thing that impresses teachers, it's well-written essays. University professors are no different, and as Einstein was churning out essays and theories by the dozen they began to take notice and be impressed. This led to him being made a professor himself – in lots of places.

Chapter 4

The travelling man

"We're on the move again."

Albert's life from 1909 seemed to be just one move after another. Look at his timetable:

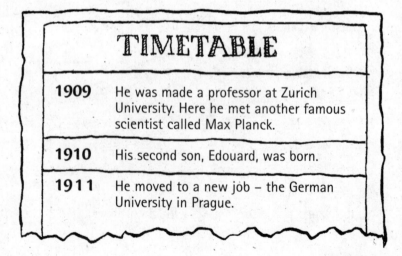

TIMETABLE

1909	He was made a professor at Zurich University. Here he met another famous scientist called Max Planck.
1910	His second son, Edouard, was born.
1911	He moved to a new job – the German University in Prague.

Scientists like to label things differently and, if possible, use long words, so to them a point of view is a *frame of reference*.

Just as two people can see the same thing from different frames of reference, so one person can see two things happening at the same time from one frame of reference, but he may not see them at the same time.

Imagine you are looking out of your window at a clear blue sky. A plane comes into view, flying low and directly towards your window. Suddenly it veers to one side and you see that behind it is another plane flying exactly the same course. Both were in your frame of reference and doing the same thing at the same time, but you couldn't see the second one because the first one was in the way!

Now, still at the same window, imagine that you are looking at two huge explosions, both happening at the same time but one explosion is on the Moon and one on the Sun. What you will actually see is one explosion on the Moon and then, later, an explosion on the Sun, even though they both happened at precisely the same second in our time. Light from the Moon reaches us faster than light from the Sun, so we see the Moon's explosion first.

Ready for this one? Here goes – the whole point about Einstein's theory of relativity is NOT that everything IS relative, but that NOT EVERYTHING is relative! There are some things that remain the same whatever your point of view (frame of reference).

Both space and time can only be measured when compared to something else. This means that time can either speed up or slow down, depending on how fast you are moving.

When you sit with a nice girl for two hours, it seems like two minutes. When you sit on a hot stove for two minutes, it seems like two hours – that's relativity.

There's more!

Isaac Newton thought that the distance between two points on a solid object is always the same, even if the object is moving and that the measurement of the time it takes to do something is always the same, because he thought of time and space as straight lines.

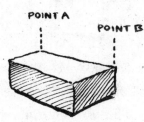

POINT A
POINT B

Einstein came along and saw space and time as a curve. Until Einstein put on his thinking cap, scientists had thought of the universe as three-dimensional.

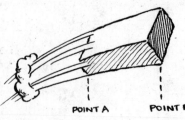

POINT A   POINT B

Einstein threw in time as another dimension that was relative to the other three. It existed only because the other three dimensions existed.

When asked by reporters in New York to explain this, he said: "It was formerly believed that if all material things disappeared out of the universe, time and space would be left.

According to relativity theory, however, time and space disappear together with the things."

TIME SPACE

PIFF

Time and space are not something in which we live, like a box into which all the bits of the universe have been put, they are a result of the way those bits work. Rather than being fixed, the universe we live in is moving and growing, as you move and grow. So sometimes, time and space may change as other things have an effect on them.

Einstein also showed that measurements of distance (space) and of time change according to your point of view (frame of reference). This is because if you are distanced from an object or event you are seeing it across a curve, not a straight line.

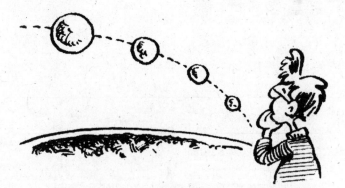

Imagine a train speeding along a straight track. A boy is standing on the bank beside the track, watching the train go by. Inside the train is another boy who can see how long the train is. To the boy outside, the train will look shorter *and really will be shorter* because the movement of the train slightly changes the curve of the space around it.

Now imagine the boy on the train has a clock on his lap. This ticks away loudly with exactly one second between the ticks. The ticking is so loud that the boy watching outside can hear it, but to him there is more than exactly one second between the ticks because the ticking sound has to reach him across a piece of curved space so it takes longer.

These differences are so tiny as to be almost impossible to notice, but if you were in a spacecraft going almost as fast as the speed of light, you'd notice them more. As objects travel nearer to the speed of light strange things happen to them. They get shorter – if an object reached the speed of light, its length would shrink to nothing. It would not disappear though because the second strange thing is that its mass (the amount of matter in it), would increase. Also, time would pass more slowly for it.

The shortest scientific way of explaining all this is that moving objects have different properties to stationary ones. Say that casually in front of one of your teachers and watch them fall over backwards in stunned respect.

So, Einstein threw a few other bits of information into Newton's pot. He added something to inertia:

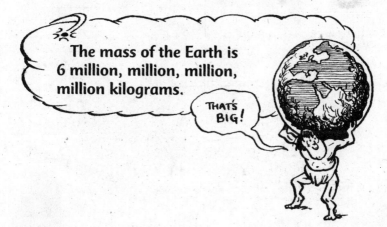

The mass of the Earth is 6 million, million, million, million kilograms.

THAT'S BIG!

> **Once every 24 hours the Earth makes one complete turn. That means that any point on Earth is actually moving at a speed of over 1600 km/h.**

If you have ever tried to eat a sandwich on a roller-coaster, you know how hard it is to do. Yet every day, as you walk to school, ride a bike, kick a ball, eat your tea, you are hurtling through space at over 1600 km an hour, and spinning as you go. You never feel a thing, or think about it because the speed is constant and everything on the planet behaves as if it were at rest.

So if you look up at a jet plane passing overhead, you can see that the plane is moving but you don't feel that you are also moving. If you knew enough maths you could work out the plane's speed as if you were standing still on something that wasn't moving, even though you actually are hurtling through space. This is because the speed of the planet you are standing on, your point of view or frame of reference is always the same. It is a constant frame of reference, a frame of inertia – Einstein said that the laws of nature must be the same in

every frame of inertia. So when things start to behave unexpectedly, you have to look for other things going on that you don't yet know about.

Having said that everything behaves the same he then, like most scientists, confused things by saying... "– except light!" (This is a good time to start practising juggling!)

I see the Light!

Einstein worked out that light travels at a constant speed and in a straight line only if there is nothing to get in the way, but it can be slowed down or pushed off course.

 water slows light to 225,000 km per second

 light passing through a diamond is slowed to a mere 125,000 km per second

Einstein also worked out that light did not travel in straight lines but bent around objects. Light from a distant star would be bent by the gravity, or energy, of the Sun and

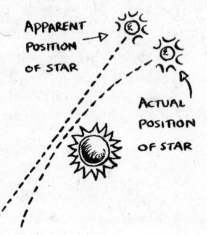

APPARENT POSITION OF STAR

ACTUAL POSITION OF STAR

so pushed into a curve. The eclipse of the Sun in 1919 conveniently gave scientists a chance to test this theory – and prove it true.

You may not shine as brightly as the sun, but you, too, can bend light. Here's what you do:

EXPERIMENT

Get a square, clear plastic container, or a jam jar, and fill it with water. Find a small torch. Put the jar in a darkish place and prop a sheet of plain paper at one side of the jar. Shine the torch through the jar from the side opposite the paper. Shine the torch either downwards or upwards, so that the beam enters the water at an angle. You will see the light ray bend in the water and come out at a different angle. To see this more clearly, stir a teaspoon of milk into the water.

TORCH

JAM JAR

CARDBOARD

WATER

A little light relief

If you were travelling at the speed of light it would take you:

 one second to circle the Earth seven times

 $1/56$ second to travel from the UK to the USA

 eight minutes to go from the Sun to the Earth

...and – you could zip past your friends at 300,000 km per second.

BYE MUM, I'LL BE BACK IN TWO SECONDS!

There was a young lady named Bright
Who travelled much
faster than light,
She started one day
In the relative way
And returned on the previous night.

Learning about light is another one of those juggling acts I told you about earlier. Light travels in tiny waves, like the waves of the sea. It also travels in teeny pieces or particles. Sometimes it does one, sometimes the other, sometimes both. Sometimes it starts out as a wave and splits into particles when an obstacle gets in its way.

Light can be seen and unseen. Light rays from the Sun, stars and electric light shine right into your eyes. Everything else you only see because light rays hit objects and bounce back off them. If light is not hitting an object you cannot see it; it looks black.

Where was Einstein when the lights went out? In the dark!

EHH!

The waves of light come in different lengths, which we see as colours. Ordinary white light, from the Sun or an electric light bulb, is made up of thousands of colours, all slightly different from each other. Human eyes can only see a very few of the colours that light actually comes in.

Brain boiling yet? Try fanning yourself with the book!

Chapter 5

"Thank you Elsa."

One day in 1917 Albert's cousin Elsa came to visit him. She was shocked when she arrived at the house.

"Albert, whatever is the matter?"

"I don't really know. I just feel – very ill."

Without saying another word Albert collapsed and had to be put to bed. He had been working far too hard. He was seriously ill.

"You can't look after yourself, that's certain," said Elsa. "I'm going to move in and nurse you."

"But...but...," gasped the struggling Albert.

"No buts – I'm doing it."

And so began another important change in Albert's life. Elsa moved in to nurse him and as he recovered he realized that he now thought of her as much more than a nurse. In 1919 he divorced Mileva and he and Elsa were married.

Also in 1919 an eclipse of the Sun very obligingly gave scientists a good chance to prove that Einstein's General Theory of Relativity worked. It

did. They tested it by photographing stars during the eclipse and comparing them with photos taken at night. The stars were in different places to where we normally see them, proving that the light from them is usually pushed off course by the Sun's gravity. Albert, a keen letter writer, wrote home about it:

Dear Mother,

Good news today. H.A. Lorentz has wired me that the British expeditions have actually proved the light deflection near the Sun.

Your loving son, Albert

XXX

Gravity

The third bit of information Einstein came up with was about gravity. Gravity is the invisible force that pulls every object in the universe towards every other object in the universe. The bigger the object, the stronger the pull of its gravity. The farther apart the objects, the weaker will be the pull of gravity on each other.

When a satellite orbits Earth, Earth's gravity is tugging it downwards all the while. It stays up because it has been put into space at exactly the right height for its speed. It goes so fast that its own force pulls against Earth's gravity and keeps it whizzing round safely.

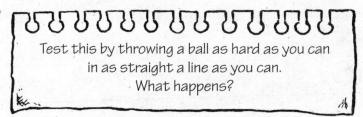

Test this by throwing a ball as hard as you can in as straight a line as you can. What happens?

The ball will travel for a short while in a straight line, then it will begin to loop towards Earth and finally fall to the ground. If you could throw your ball with enough force to pull against Earth's gravity long enough, it would keep going right round the Earth until it came back to you.

You must throw a ball at a speed of 39,600 km/h in order for it to escape Earth's gravity and enter space

Einstein said that the gravity of any object, such as our Sun, pushed or warped the space and time around it.

Think of space and time as a river flowing happily along until it comes to a rock. Then the water splits and flows around the rock to the other side.

Or, imagine you and a friend are holding a table cloth between you, each at one end, with the cloth held as flat as you can, Then another friend comes along and drops a cricket ball on the cloth. What happens? The cloth sags into a sort of U-shape to bear the weight of the ball.

Both those things are what happens to space and time around large objects.

You see, Einstein wasn't interested so much in the objects themselves, as to what happened in the space between and around the objects – and this is what he thinks happens.

The matter and energy, all the stuff of the universe, actually mould the shape of space and the flow of time. What we feel as the force of gravity is simply the feeling of everything following

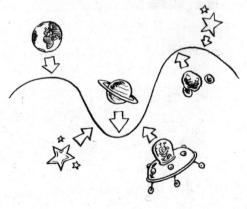

the shortest path it can through curved space and time. A sort of cosmic, curving, flowing dance.

If all this is making your mind boggle – you're in good company.

Einstein said:

> **"When the Theory of Relativity began to take shape inside me, I was visited by all sorts of nervous conflicts... I used to go away for weeks in a state of confusion."**

Gravity guide

Hydroelectric power depends on the fact that water is drawn downwards by gravity to turn the turbine that generates electricity.

What we call weight is the effect of the pull of gravity. A person on an aeroplane would not weigh as much as he would weigh on the ground because the pull of gravity on him would be weaker. The further from the surface of the Earth, the weaker the pull of gravity.

Gravity cannot be held responsible for people falling in love.

THUMP

When an astronaut orbits the Earth he is weightless. Earth orbits the Sun and in that position it is weightless.

The gravity on the surface of the Moon is less than the gravity on Earth. Someone who weighs 78 kilograms on Earth would weigh 12 kilograms on the moon.

Objects falling towards the ground fall faster and faster because they are accelerated by the pull of gravity – i.e. the nearer they get to the surface the stronger the pull.

A rocket going into space from Earth needs to blast off at 39,600 km/h to have enough force to escape the pull of Earth's gravity.

The force of the Moon's gravity is strong enough to pull at the seas of the Earth and cause the daily tides.

If you jump off a wall the Earth pulls you towards the ground. You also pull the Earth towards you, but as you are much smaller than the Earth, it has the strongest pull – so you move the most.

All of these ideas of Einstein's gave people something to think about other than the war that had been going on for the last five years. His theories became well-known.

Chapter 6

The winner!

Once the war was over Albert was on his travels again – and then he heard the great news!

The newspaper headlines told the world. The Nobel Prize is tremendously famous. It is awarded to people who do great work in different areas. In 1922 Albert won it for his work in physics.

He was now more famous than ever.

Albert used his scientific fame in another way. Wherever he went – England, France, Austria, South America, Japan, Palestine, Spain – he spoke about peace.

"We must never have war again," he proclaimed. "Man must have peace."

Yet Einstein still searched for his Grand Unified Theory that would explain and link everything. He carried on this search for much of the rest of his life

How much?

Scientists enjoy taking each other's theories and pulling them to pieces or adding bits of their own. A German scientist, Max Planck, discovered that light travels as small bits. He called these small packages of light *quanta*, which is Latin for 'how much?' That's a scientist's way of saying "I don't know much about this!" In 1924 Einstein added his bit to the new quantum theory.

He said it was:

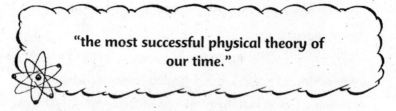

"the most successful physical theory of our time."

This theory, which he had helped to create, could explain nearly all the 'hows' and 'whys' that scientists asked. Lots of our modern gadgets such as transistors and lasers have come from an understanding of quantum science.

Einstein found out a bit more about these packages of

light and realised that sometimes light travels as waves and sometimes as small bits (particles).

Once they knew teeny pieces of this and that existed, modern scientists leapt on them with enthusiasm and so quantum mechanics was born.

Quantum mechanics

Quantum mechanics looks at the very small, the teeniest parts of the universe. It describes how single atoms and atomic particles behave.

Imagine you are in a French art gallery looking at a large painting by an impressionist artist. You look at a beautiful picture of a garden full of flowers, painted in bright patches of colour.

Then you walk right up to the painting until your nose is almost pressing against it and you see that every patch of colour is made up of a chaotic mass of teeny coloured dots and splodges. From a distance it looks like one thing, but

close-up it looks like another.

That's exactly what quantum scientists do. They walk right up to things, peer closely and find that what looks like order and neatness from a distance is really made up of a chaotic movement of teeny bits. They look inside the bits.

Small but strange

 Remember Newton's third law – every action results in an equal opposite reaction? Well, not in this world of teeny-weeny. Here two exactly identical actions can get quite different results.

 Electrons (some of the small bits) are shape-shifters. Sometimes they behave like a particle and then, just to fool you, they behave like a wave.

 One of the strangest things about some of these small particles is that they do different things when they are being watched than when they are not being watched.

Some scientists believe that every time a small particle of energy, like an electron, is faced with a choice it chooses both – and another reality is created, one in which it does A and one in which it does B. What if it is possible to see both of those realities?

Perhaps lots of different Universes exist at the same time – parallel realities, a new one created every time an electron splits and makes two choices.

Maybe all times exist at once.

Maybe time is a spiral of energy that you can slip up and down, like a fireman's pole.

Maybe time is a grid that you can move to any point on if you know the co-ordinates.

History is full of stories of time-slips, if you look for them. Here's one:

In 1896 a shy, seven-year-old boy at boarding school had been beaten by his cruel headmaster. Hurt and upset he ran off after lunch and wandered round the town until he came to a street that ended in a high wall in which was a door. Going through the door the boy found himself in another street with houses unlike any he had seen before. All the houses were empty. Cautiously he explored and went right inside one house, climbing the stairs to a big, empty room at the top. Crossing to its large window he gazed out over land sloping away to a valley and beyond that, to low, tree-

covered hills. He recognised none of it. Puzzled, he went back to school. For months he searched but he never found the door in the wall or that street again.

Twenty-one years later the boy, now grown-up and a soldier fighting in World War One, was in France, near the River Somme. One evening he decided to explore the area. Wandering along, he came to a village called Misery, now deserted. His hair stood on end. He was in the street he had explored all those years ago as an unhappy little boy. One house attracted him. He went in and climbed the stairs. He found himself in the large room he had been in before, looking out on the view he had seen years ago.

How do things like this happen? There are many theories. Why not come up with some of your own? That's what Einstein did – then he used maths and reasoning to see if his theories would work – but everything he discovered started as an idea in his head.

Not out, but in

Nearly a century after Einstein changed humankind's understanding of nature and the universe, trying to solve those puzzles he could not crack. Now instead of looking out, they are looking in.

Chapter 7

A terrible time

"RAUS!"

Another German word. And a dreadful one if you were a Jew living in Germany in 1933. It means "Get out!"

That's what the Nazis wanted all Jews to do. The Nazis were the new government of Germany. They hated Jews. They took their jobs and their money and their homes away from them. Eventually they started killing them.

Can you imagine how Albert felt?

He was a Jew, and a world famous one at that. He was also a German – but now his country had no time for him.

Sadly he left and took a job in a university in America.
Just in time! In October, 1933, the Nazis seized his home. As
long as they were in power he could never go back to
Germany.

Now began another very busy time for Albert.

He did everything he could to help make the world a more
peaceful place. He spoke to many groups in America. He
even joined an international protest to save the lives of
eight black men from Alabama who had been wrongly
convicted of a crime.

And so to England.

"The Nazis are a danger to the world."
Winston Churchill was one of the famous
politicians Albert said this to.

But being Albert, strange as well as important things kept
happening to him. One of the 'strange' things was funny,
one dramatic.

He became very friendly with David Rothman, who owned
a big department store in New York. This friendship started
when Albert went into the shop and asked for 'sundials'.

David had none in the store, but he did have one in his
own garden. He took Albert there and offered it to him.

Albert looked at him in amazement.

"I don't want that!" he gasped. "I want sundials to put on my feet!"

Of course he meant 'sandals'.

David Rothman thought that this was so funny that he sent Albert a pair of sandals every year from then on.

The other 'strange' thing was scary.

Albert liked sailing his boat off Long Island. Being Albert of course he was a sailor who couldn't swim! One day he fell overboard.

"I'm drowning, I'm drowning!" he gasped helplessly.

He thought his life was over. Then, miraculously, he was hauled out by a passing teenager.

Albert was always sorry he could never say a proper thank you to his rescuer – but the boy went on his way without even leaving his name.

Weapons of doom

A group of nuclear scientists came to see Albert with an important matter to discuss.

"I agree with you," said Albert, after he had talked to them. "I think the Nazis will try and make an atomic bomb. We must tell President Roosevelt."

This was in 1939. So America went on to develop and use the first atomic bomb.

In August of 1945 the first atomic bombs were dropped on the Japanese cities of Hiroshima and Nagasaki by the USA.

The detonation of a large nuclear bomb above ground creates a huge mushroom cloud of radioactive dust and debris above the explosion that can reach several kilometres in height. Millions of people die and everything over a wide area is destroyed.

A 15 megaton nuclear bomb will cause all flammable material, within 20 kilometres to burst into flames.

The first hydrogen bomb was tested in 1952 and from then on the USA and Russia were in a race to see who could make the first and the most nuclear weapons.

Although much of Einstein's work led to the development of nuclear weapons he was a kind, peaceful man who cared about the planet and its creatures. He said, "Human health and the chances for the survival of life on earth will benefit best if people change to a vegetarian diet."

Einstein was against the use of such terrible weapons. In 1941 he joined in with a group of scientists who tried to persuade the world's governments not to continue to make and use them.

Chapter 8

Another great honour

"Will you be president of our country?"

Who said this, and why, you might ask.

Well, as soon as World War Two was over Albert began reminding everybody about how dreadfully the Jews had suffered – and how few people had been prepared to help them.

In 1948 the state of Israel was created. This enabled Jews to have a country of their own. In 1952 Albert Einstein was asked to become the second president of the state.

"No thank you."

This was what Albert said in reply. The invitation was a huge honour but he felt he could do more to help Jews by supporting groups throughout the world who were working towards permanent peace.

So – as Albert got towards the end of his life – what can we say about him as a man?

A great and good genius

We couldn't forget how he looked for a start. With his mass of wild white hair he looked every inch the mad professor. We also know that he was one of the most famous men who ever lived, and here is a reminder of that. March 14th was his birthday. On this day at the peak of his fame, he received hundreds and hundreds of letters, cards and telegrams.
They came from all over the world.

SCRATCH

Then let's remember that he hadn't been much good at school. This of course didn't mean that he wasn't thinking. He certainly was!

For instance when he was only 12 he realized that not everything in the Bible could be true. But, at the same time, he believed that the universe had been created. Albert thought this had been done by "a superior spirit who reveals himself in all the small details of the universe."

He went on to say,

> **"We should get to know more about all living creatures and the whole nature of the world's beauty."**

Albert believed in this very strongly. He thought the more we knew about the Earth, animals, birds, plants, trees and stars the more we would understand the world.

"We're just not closely enough connected to them," he used to say.

There were a few things Albert would have liked us all to do. For instance he might have said:

"Get a pet, care for it and bring it up.
Start growing a plant from a seed.
Study a tree and see how it changes through the seasons.
Look at the stars as carefully as you can."

Albert had a great sense of wonder at the mysteries all around us.
"They are the source of all true art and science," he said.
Nobody could ever accuse Albert of being a dull man!

He gave us so much to think about. For instance...

 Just 1 kilogram of matter can produce as much energy as a major earthquake

 The atoms used to make nuclear energy are those found in uranium, plutonium and deuterium (a type of hydrogen)

 One kilogram of deuterium can produce as much energy as three million kilograms of coal

 All the stars, including our Sun, get their energy from nuclear fusion

 Nuclear power stations make huge amounts of power with just a few tonnes of nuclear fuel

 When energy is made by nuclear fission lots of waste products are left. These are very dangerous and stay that way for thousands of years, so they can't just be thrown away but have to stored carefully deep in the ground or under the sea.

Even when he was world famous he was still as inquisitive and excited about things as he had been as a schoolboy. He might have shaken his woolly head at us and said

"Never...never...never stop asking questions, and never ever stop using your imagination."

Albert Einstein died on April 18th, 1955. There was even a little mystery surrounding his death. He spoke a last few words to his nurse. But we'll never know what he said. He spoke in German and his nurse couldn't understand the language!

As we said at the beginning Albert's fantastic brain was kept after his death. It is still in pieces in jars. Some of it is in Philadelphia, some in California, some in New Jersey. It is all in the USA. Even his eyes were kept.

Not all good news

Energy makes things happen. Without energy you could not live or move.

Tiny atoms contain huge amounts of energy.

This is called nuclear energy because most of it comes from the nucleus – or middle bit – of an atom.

Einstein showed that matter could be changed into energy. When energy is made in this way some, but not a lot, of matter disappears. A tiny loss of matter makes a huge amount of energy.

Mankind has used this knowledge to create energy for making electricity and also for making weapons.

Nuclear power

Nuclear power is energy produced by splitting the nucleus of uranium atoms. This is done by putting the atoms inside a machine called a nuclear reactor and hurling at them particles called neutrons. The energy released is used to produce steam which drives a steam turbine which generates electricity.

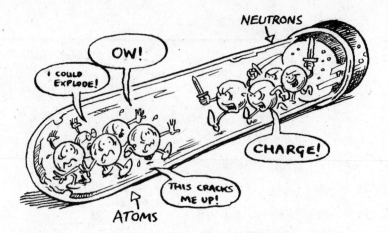

NEUTRONS

OW!

I COULD EXPLODE!

CHARGE!

THIS CRACKS ME UP!

ATOMS

An atom bomb explodes when the large nuclei (middle bits) inside the atoms split apart and the small amount of mass changes into energy. This is called nuclear fission.

A hydrogen bomb explodes when the light atomic nuclei inside it are mixed to form one large nucleus. The nuclear energy released in this way is even greater than when atoms are split and this process is called nuclear fusion.

Black holes

Welcome to the dark side! I'm glad to see you've brought your friend and the tablecloth. Spread it out again and each hold an end. This time, instead of dropping a cricket ball into the centre of the table cloth you drop a ball that can be any size but that is so heavy that it pulls the table cloth right up around it and yanks the two of you to the floor

mass: the amount of material in an object.

Nobel Prize: A prize given each year to people who have done something great to help the planet. It is named after Alfred Nobel who donated the money for the prizes.

nuclear: the middle bit of an atom

particle: a speck

pathologist: surgeon

philosopher: someone who thinks deeply about the universe

physics: the study of matter and energy

physicist: a scientist who studies matter and energy.

research: study, investigation

theory: An idea or opinion which has yet to be proved to be true.

Science notes

Science notes

other titles in the same series